OUT OF PICTURE

ART FROM THE OUTSIDE LOOKING IN

OUT OF PICTURE

ART FROM THE OUTSIDE LOOKING IN

OUT OF PICTURE, April 2006. First Printing.

Masterminds: Daisuke Tsutsumi, Vincent Nguyen
Cover Art by Michael Knapp and Daisuke Tsutsumi
Back Cover Illustration by Daniel Lòpez Muñoz
Book Design: Michael Knapp

ISBN Number 0-9772449-0-3

TABLE OF
(MAL)
CONTENTS

Illustration by Vincent Nguyen
Drawing on previous page by Vincent Nguyen

FOREWORD

The artists at Blue Sky exist in a community of collaboration. They dance for years at a time, around a monster called an animated movie. They whisper what it might become into the ether around the operating table. They lay its bones down one by one. They dress it carefully in flesh, and caress the heart of it to bring it to life. Whether it stands and walks, or drops in confused convulsions will not be known until they are finished, but it will do so at the feet of these many surrogate parents, entranced at what they have wrought together.

This process by which each contributes a focused ray of their own talent, then steps aside to allow the next the same is one of measured sacrifice. In giving only what is asked of them, each holds back a reservoir of creative potential that roils, impatient for escape, within their hearts.

Ironically the worlds that exist within each one of them are as complete as the worlds they create together. This truth I relearn in every interaction in every moment at Blue Sky – that our endeavors together are fed by wells of limitless creativity that exist inside each one of us, and that what forms as complete work outside is a shadow of that potential concealed within.

Here then lies a glimpse into the realms which these wizards normally protect for themselves. Released from the laboratory, they have conspired to offer their own stories in their own hands, on their own terms. They have admitted us into a secret circle where each in turn howls at the moon in their own voice.

It is as much a privilege for me to work with these artists as it is to present them to you. They are the means by which our movies are conceived, and by which the future of our medium is undoubtedly assured.

CHRIS WEDGE
DIRECTOR, BLUE SKY STUDIOS
SEPTEMBER 2005

Illustration by Andrea Blasich

Previous spread from left to right, top to bottom: Daniel Lòpez Muñoz, Benoit Le Pennec, Nash Dunnigan, Daisuke Tsutsumi, Vincent Nguyen, Greg Couch, Robert Mackenzie, Peter de Sève, Michael Knapp, David Gordon, and Andrea Blasich.

"Out of picture" is a film term we use whenever something is cut from a movie - or we say "it's OOPed". While it can be frustrating to have to let go of one's ideas, it's the pursuit and exploration of those ideas that can be the most fulfilling. We wanted to share some of our personal ideas outside of our film work with you - out of picture...

We hope you enjoy them.

DAISUKE TSUTSUMI

---Shadow...?

---Constantly I feel shadow over my chest....

---Medicatoin or therapy?

---I've tried all those.....

And you know I have an unconventional technique?

But you get your job done.

dice tsutsumi

NOCHE y DIA

close your eyes..

Relax...Señora Lopez, we are coming in......

--there's nothing to be scared of....

--Mama, please don't turn off the light

--sweetie, we have to turn the light off.

Papa...? Please, Papa...?

--There's nothing to be scared of, chiquita.
As a matter of fact, did you know Day and Night were twins?

---Really...?

---They can't exist without one another.
So there's nothing to be scared of.....

--sweet dreams chiquita..

--end...

HEY, DIDDLE, DIDDLE

Hey, diddle, diddle!
The cat and the fiddle,

LITTLE BO-PEEP

Little Bo-Peep has lost her sheep,
And can't tell where to find
them;
Leave them al

HUMPTY

Humpty Dumpty sat o
umpty Dumpty had a
the King's hors
ing's men
put Humpty

Sing a song of sixpence,
A pocket full of rye;
Four-and-twenty blackbirds
Baked in a pie!

When the pie was opened
The birds began to sing;
'as not that a dainty dish
before the king?

was in his counting-house,
ing out his money;
ueen was in the parlor,
ing bread and honey.

maid was in the garden,
Hanging out the clothes;
hen down came a blackbird
And snapped off her nose.

LITTLE JACK HORNER

Little Jack Horner
Sat in the corner,
Eating of Christmas pie;
le put in his thumb,
d pulled out a
And sa

GREG COUCH

From the pen of Mother Goose...

...comes a bedtime story so nightmarish, it could only be told through Nursery Rhymes!

I know ... because it's my story. My name's Horner. "Little" Jack Horner. I'm a private eye . . .

. . . .and I've stuck my thumbs into too many pies and come up plumless, to ever risk my my digits again.

Murder!

That's my partner, Jack Nimble, lying there dead by the bushes of Mulberry Park. It should be me. He was doing legwork on my case. He usually stayed on his toes...

Listen, Horner... As Chief of Police, it's my duty to tell you - you're playing with fire! That was no candle you had Nimble jump over - it was a stick of dynamite! Someone dealt your partner a lousy hand and I think you know who!

Intrigue!

Just who tripped Nimble up, and why? What did they want from him, that got him burned?

I needed answers fast, and the only one who can help unravel this mess is the same one who started this tangled ball of yarn rolling, the day she walked into the office . . .

But is SHE the one pulling the strings?. . . . Can she be trusted? . . . . . Who is she, really . . . .

MICHAEL KNAPP

CAR BOMB IN TIKRIT WOUNDED SEVERAL

IN OTHER NEWS...

BENOIT LE PENNEC

...OF FLOATING HOLIDAYS.   BENOIT 05

OUT **OF PICTURE**

DANIEL LÒPEZ MUÑOZ

WHEN I WAS A LITTLE BOY, I READ A LEGEND UNDER MY BED. I READ IT IN FRAGMENTS, EVERY NIGHT FOR A WEEK, HIDING IT AMONGST MY SCHOOLBOOKS. I HAD STOLEN IT FROM MY GRANDFATHER'S BOOKSHELF. IT WAS ONE OF THOSE OLD BOOKS NOT MEANT FOR US CHILDREN TO READ, BUT UP ON THAT SHELF IT INVITED THE OCCASION.

SILENT ECHOES

CHAPTER 1

IT TOLD OF THE MAN OF THE LOST CITY OF BUENDONÁ, IN THE CENTRAL CORDILLERA, WHO ONCE ROSE INTO THE SKY. AND FROM ON HIGH CONTEMPLATED THE EARTH BELOW.

OF HIS JOURNEY HE PROCLAIMED TO HAVE UNDERSTOOD HUMAN LIFE FROM ABOVE. "WE ARE ALL HAUNTED BY THE RESONATING ECHOES OF OUR PAST." HE REVEALED, "AND ERRATICALLY WE RIDE THE FADING RIPPLES OF OUR LIVES . . ."

QUINTO LEVANTE ANSWERED THE RUMBLINGS OF HIS MIND,

FOLLOWED THE DISTANT VOICES HE HAD HEARD WITH HIS EYES WHEN HE WAS A CHILD.

AND IN THE SEVENTEENTH WINTER OF HIS YOUTH HE LEFT THE SEMINARY TO ENTER THE JUNGLE.

RUMORS FOUND HIM YEARS LATER WITH COMANDANTE **ARROYO TIROFIRME**, WHO ONCE GAVE **QUINTO** HIS LIFE IN SPITE OF THE RAVENOUS DEATH THAT ATE THE FLESH OF HIS PARENT'S YOUTH.

SPITEFUL DARK DAYS OF "LA VIOLENCIA".

IN SEARCH OF PHANTOMS, **QUINTO** FORCED HIS BODY ACROSS THE FEVERISH RIVERS AND THROUGH THE FORGOTTEN JUNGLES OF THE **CHAGUÁN**. TO GIVE HIS LIFE BACK TO HIS MORTAL SAVIOR.

TO QUIET PERHAPS, THE DISTANT VOICES OF HIS PAST.

QUINTO SERVED THE NEXT FEW YEARS IN THE PEASANT TOWN OF **BUENDONÁ**, NEAR SAN JOSÉ DEL CHAGUÁN. HER SONS SURRENDERED TO THE REVOLUTION ...

... IN EXCHANGE FOR THE PROMISE OF A GASPING DREAM.

PETER DE SÈVE

DAVID GORDON

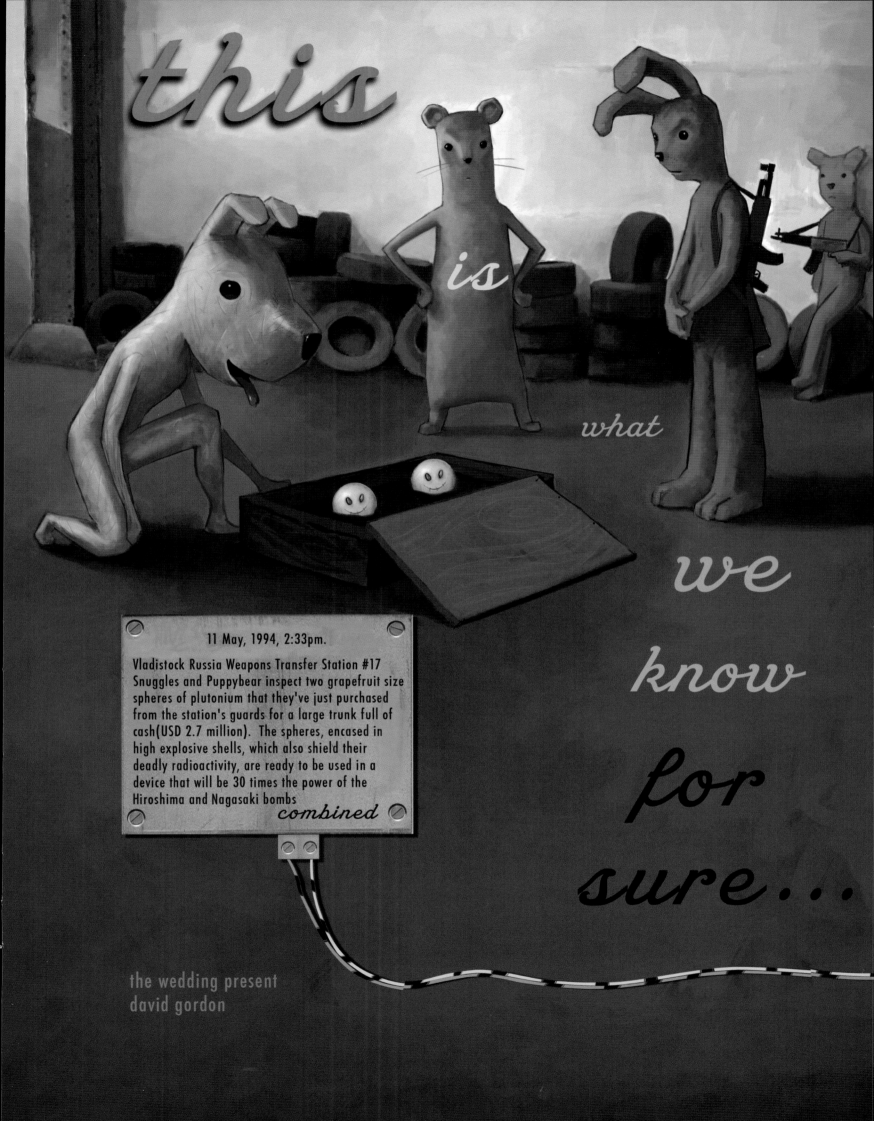

this is what we know for sure...

11 May, 1994, 2:33pm.

Vladistock Russia Weapons Transfer Station #17 Snuggles and Puppybear inspect two grapefruit size spheres of plutonium that they've just purchased from the station's guards for a large trunk full of cash(USD 2.7 million). The spheres, encased in high explosive shells, which also shield their deadly radioactivity, are ready to be used in a device that will be 30 times the power of the Hiroshima and Nagasaki bombs combined

the wedding present
david gordon

...Snuggles sent us a Fuckbomb.

photo reference: Morton Beebe

23 December, 1996, 4:56:23 and 11:04:52 pm . Oakland, Ca.   A P&O Nedlloyd
Container ship arrives in San Francisco after an 8 day journey from Quingdao, China.
Container #433EY-23 is packed with 450 drums of processed sorghum. Hidden within
one of them are the two spheres of plutonium. Later, at the MacArthur Bart Station,
Pookie Wabbit waits of and unknown al Queda operative to meet him and take him
to a safehouse in Fremont. In his briefcase he carries the spheres and a circuit board
made by an electronics engineer in Cairo that will be used as part of the primary
trigger for the device now referred to in code as "the wedding present"

But,

11 Sept, 2001. 5:16:17 pm. Nutley NJ, and 14 Sept, 2001, 8:50:10 am Denver CO The wedding present is moved from one safehouse to the another.

14 April, 1999. 4:55:11 pm. Guanajuato, Mexico. Lil Darlin walks to the station to catch a bus to San Diego. He's been told he's the trigger man.

23 August, 1998, 3:13:56. 27 miles northwest of Old Ramireno, Texas. Sugar Pup and four Mexicans are apprehended off hwy 83 by border patrol officer Bruce Mensink. Pup is carrying a backup circuit board (hidden in a radio) for the wedding present. He's arrested, held by overworked border agents for 4 hours and sent back to Mexico. he sucessfully crosses the border again near Nogales the next day.

what we

In the months and years following September 11th, all al Queda activity in the US went to "sleep". The Wedding Present was moved from safe house to safe

house. For the next five years, various parts of the device were fabricated,

don't

tested, perfected, tested again and assembled in garages, apartments and

back rooms from Senegal to Seattle, hidden and completely undetected.

Tobaccohol

Meanwhile, after years of recession, depression, civil unrest, and the near collapse of global trade from skyrocketing energy costs, America's chief export became Tobaccohol - a potent and highly addictive beverage demanded and consumed by billions worldwide.

Warning: contents under pressure. For internal use only. Keep away from children under 8 months of age. Keep away from genitals and other mucous membranes. Contains petroleum distillates, narcotic hydantoin, polycarbonate organic esters, mercurial isoflavonoids, dimethelethelanalsurrogatereductous lubricants and conjunctive bimethane precalsigent viscosity agents that are known in the state of Oklahoma to cause arachnid histopathological carcinoma variants among blue bottle blowflies. If injecting, use fresh veins. Do not mix with meth-amphetamine, cocaine or oxycontin without the strict supervision of a parent or doctor. If an unpleasant odor is detected emenating from the scalp 3 days after use, call poison control immediately. Do not consume for more than 4 weeks.

know

14 January, 2009, 45 miles northwest of Buraydah, Saudi Arabia. The earth's one-time endowment of light, sweet crude is almost gone. The Saudis, desperate for oil revenue and food for their starving population have resorted to raising "coil", a hideous feat of bioengineering whereby a cow, after being fed enough petrobiotics is then able to excrete a high-sulpher bio-oil("boil") suitable for refinement into gasoline, kerosene and rocket fuel.

or

care

15 June, 2010, 5:45:07am. Blackfeet Indian reservation, 145 miles west of Sweetgrass, Montana. Snuffy and Bubbles cross the US/Canadian border with backup componants for the wedding present. These pieces, trigger housing assembly, trigger electronics and instruments to calibrate them are essential to a successful detonation of the device.

3 November, 2009. 3:33:24, New York City. Plans to detonate the wedding present on September 11th, the 8th anniversary of the attacks on the World Trade Center and the Pentagon, were postponed. Snuggles authorizes Tickles to deliver the last fifty thousand dollars, in cash, to cover continuing operational costs.

to *know* *is*

3 December, 12:13:34, 6 December 10:54:01 and 8 December 3:00:59 (2010) New York City, Rome, Washington state respectively. For almost 14 years screw by screw, wire by wire, al Queda operatives patiently and meticulously disassembeled, smuggled and then reassembled a nuclear weapon in the United States without being detected. In the nine years since Sept 11, and in the absence of another terrorist attack on our soil, the US government's spending on homeland security equaled one DAY of the cost of fighting in the ongoing wars in Korea, Iran and Iraq. And it wasn't as if we weren't warned, or had no idea that this could, or would happen.

ANDREA BLASICH

VINCENT NGUYEN

DOMESTICITY

NASH DUNNIGAN

ALL I'M SAYING IS THAT I REMEMBER A TIME WHEN THE CHURCH KEPT TO IT'S OWN BUSINESS. LOOKIN' AFTER PEOPLES WELL BEING, COMMUNITIES HELPIN EACH OTHER OUT. GOVERNMENT DIDN'T NEED TO POKE IT'S NOSE IN THAT...

KNOCK IT OFF! WHAT IF THE BRATS COME BACK?

WHEN WAS IT, WILKES? THIRTY OF FOURTY YEARS AGO? IT ALL STARTED OFF FRIENDLY ENOUGH. THE GOVERNMENT PUTTIN' ON A MORE MORAL AND WHOLESOME FACE. THAT SEEMED TO MAKE EVERYBODY HAPPY, REMEMBER? EVERYBODY WAS GETTIN' BEHIND IT...

BUT, REMEMBER THAT ANTI-EVOLUTION SHOWDOWN IN 2112? IT WAS "SCIENTISTS VERSUS 'GENE' THE CREATIONIST DINO" AT THE SUPREME COURT.

THAT 50 FOOT INFLATABLE CHIMP WASN'T THE ONLY THING TO GET THE WIND KNOCKED OUT OF IT THAT DAY...

THINGS CHANGED....IT WAS QUIET, ALMOST NOBODY NOTICED. THE GOVERNMENT STARTED PICKIN UP THE TAB FOR THOSE 'FAITH BASED INITIATIVES.' THEY GOT TO CHOOSE WHICH ONES, TOO. BUT WHO WAS WATCHING THEM? YOU REMEMBER THAT PRESIDENT? USED TO SAY THINGS LIKE," OUR RIGHTS ARE DERIVED FROM THE BIBLE," AND THAT IT WAS THEIR,"GUIDEBOOK FOR GOOD GOVERNMENT..." THAT WAS BEFORE THE BIG WAR STARTED WHEN PATRIOTISM GOT ALL MIXED UP WITH RIGHTEOUSNESS AND THEIR HOLY MISSION. WE'VE BEEN LIVIN' WITH THAT MESS FOR GOIN ON FOURTY YEARS...

UNCLE SAM HAD BEEN RUNNIN' LOW ON CASH, WARS WERE EXPENSIVE AFTER ALL. SO BACK HERE THEY START ENLISTING THOSE LOCAL THEOCRATS AND THEIR KIDS TO KEEP THE PEACE ON THE HOMEFRONT. SEEMED LIKE A GOOD IDEA? BUT THOSE LITTLE BUGGERS GOT A SENSE OF ENTITLEMENT, LIKE THEY WERE BETTER THAN EVERYBODY ELSE. STARTED CALLIN' THEMSELVES, 'THEOBRATS.' THEY DIDN'T EVEN NEED TO PAY THEM, JUST RETURN SOME FAVORS...

NOW LOOK AT US! MY GRANDSON HAS TO SNEAK OFF TO GOD KNOWS WHERE IN THE MIDDLE OF THE NIGHT, JUST TO LEARN THE STUFF HE WON'T GET IN SCHOOL ANYMORE...

BE CAREFUL...

DON'T WORRY, I'LL BE FINE

ROBERT MACKENZIE

AROUND THE CORNER

Welcome!
You have finally
arrived. This
place might seem
a little scary,
but don't be
afraid.

but first, you must look both ways.

Things move a little quicker out here, but if you take time to reach out to others...

you will make such wonderful friends.

The city is filled with so many characters...

but be careful.

There is a difference between having character and being a character.

Just keep all of your valuables close to you, and everything will be fine.

On those days, when the
clouds have bottled up
the light —

Don't look so down.

Look Within.

Look ahead.

The world you've imagined,
is waiting for you.

BIOGRAPHIES

ANDREA BLASICH

Born in 1967, Andrea Blasich grew up in Milan, Italy. From an early age he was dedicated to art. His mom still remembers when she found Andrea drawing at three O'clock in the morning. Growing up in Italy certainly influenced Andrea's artistic view greatly. In 1990 at the Academy of Brera while studying Scenography, he discoverd a new way of expression that would influence his entire life: Animation. This passion embraced Andrea on a journey around Europe and eventually to the United States. His first "real" job was in Munich, Germany for "Munich Animation". Then in London, UK , where he worked for Warner Bros until 1997 when he had the opportunity to come to the U.S.A. to work for Dreamworks. The "dream had come true." He spent five years working in the Art Department as a Character Sculptor, Visual Development and Layout Artist for movies such as " The Road to El Dorado," "Spirit: Stallion of the Cimarron," "Sinbad" and "Shark Tale". In 2003, he and his family moved to New York where he worked on "Robots" and "Ice Age 2" at Blue Sky Studios. There he met an incredible group of artists and friends from which he learned a lot.

www.andreablasich.com
http://andreablasich.blogspot.com

GREG COUCH

At a very early age, Greg Couch was regaled with stories of the infamous Algonquin Round Table and its habituates. As such, he became obsessed the works of Dorothy Parker and Dashiell Hammett. Sadly, Greg emulated their drawing styles instead of their written works, which left him at a certain disadvantage professionally. Greg has a thirteen year-old daughter whom he adores. He ate a bug once.

PETER de SÈVE

Peter de Sève has been drawing pictures for a living for the last thirty years and is still trying to get the hang of it. He wants to take the space here to officially thank his Blue Sky pals for inviting him to be a part of this wonderful book and for their limitless patience in waiting for his meager contribution. The story, The Mermaid, is based on a traditional sea song sung by Dan Zanes, from a terrific collection of shanties called Sea Music published by Festival Five Records.

www.peterdeseve.com

NASH DUNNIGAN

Nash Dunnigan spent much of his youth inside drawing, which would explain his severe allergies to all things natural that he might have encountered outdoors. Pale, tall, and curious, he made his way to art school in 1987, to the moderately sized city of Richmond, Virginia, only to be prematurely ejected after four years and a BFA diploma in 1991. Seeking all the glory and fame that goes with a jet-set illustration career, he moved to New York, and promptly starved. But the artificial climes of a bustling metropolis suited him well, toughened him up, and he eventually clawed his way into the nurturing arms of mother animation. Revived and determined, he landed the envious(?) position of bacground/layout designer and art director at many a New York animation studio. Heck, he even helped start one. Ah, life was good. He basked in the glory of 70 hour work weeks and no overtime pay on the hot granite slab of New York for ten years... Could it get much better? In 2003, life began again, and not but 40 miles outside of New York, a studio found him in a humble portfolio thatched from reeds on the banks of the Hudson. They took him in. Their name was Blue Sky, and they called their gangly, wide-eyed bundle "Layout Artist." Here, he grew up among art-giants, practiced the art of cinematography on wonderous moving pictures like ICE AGE 2 and ROBOTS, and learned many things. They even let him be in their super-cool art book, OOP.

DAVID GORDON

Dave Gordon is a children's book author and illustrator who has a passion for airplanes, trucks, tractors, construction equipment and other cool heavy machinery. He was born and raised in Colorado and later moved to the big city to attend Parsons School of Design in New York. After graduating, Dave moved out to northern California where he created concept art for many of Pixar's films. He also worked on the acclaimed animated television series "SpongeBob" and Bluesky's "Robots".

Dave has authored and illustrated three vehicle fairy tales for Harper Collins: "The Ugly Truckling", "The Three Little Rigs" and "Hansel And Diesel". Dave now lives in New York City with his lovely girlfriend Susan and their dog Subway.

www.illustrationranch.com

MICHAEL KNAPP

Born in 1972, Michael Knapp grew up in Wilkinsburg, Pennsylvania just outside of Pittsburgh. Inspired by films (mostly Star Wars) and many cartoons (The Jungle Book, The Hobbit, and Battle For the Planets to name a few), drawing was a manic practice from a very early age. While growing up, he devoted many weekends to art classes at the Carnegie Museum and Carnegie Mellon University before attending Ringling School of Art and Design in Sarasota, Florida. In 1995, with his BFA under his belt, he began his career as a freelance illustrator in Pittsburgh before moving to New York City in 1999 where he now works as a concept artist/designer at Blue Sky Studios. He has designed for Robots, Ice Age 2 and also art directed the Scrat short "No Time For Nuts."

www.michaelknapp.com

BENOIT LE PENNEC

Born in France in 1962, Benoit was raised mostly on comic books. After studying Graphic Art in Paris, he gained experience working for both publicity agencies and TV animation studios. He then moved to London to work on the movie Balto (a 2D animated feature) for Amblimation. When that company dissolved into Dreamworks California, he moved along with many of his colleagues to the United States where he had the chance to work on all of Dreamworks 2D movies (from The Prince of Egypt to Sinbad) as a layout Artist. He recently had the opportunity to work at Bluesky Studios on "Robots"and got to meet the great talents of that neat east coast studio. Thanks to them!

DANIEL LÒPEZ MUÑOZ

Daniel López Muñoz grew up in Córdova, Spain. At age 5 a wandering pencil falls into his hands. Enchanted by its magic, Daniel never lets it go. The happy pair is now found at Pixar Animation Studios, where their love continues to grow.

ROBERT MACKENZIE

Robert MacKenzie grew up in San Mateo, California. At the age of five, he discovered that being either Santa Claus or the Easter Bunny was an unrealistic career goal, so he decided that he wanted to draw cartoons instead. He has been drawing ever since. In 1998, Robert graduated from San Jose State University with a degree in Illustration and has worked as a Concept, Visual Development and Color Key artist at Lucasfilm, PDI Dreamworks and Blue Sky Studios. Prior to moving to New York, he was on the faculty of the School of Art and Design at San Jose State.

mackenzieart@yahoo.com

VINCENT NGUYEN

Vincent Nguyen grew up in Houston, Texas, where he began his art career drawing cowboys, monsters, and superheroes. Frustrated by his inability to draw Aquaman riding a six-headed seahorse, he decided to attend the School of Visual Arts in New York, where he earned his BFA in illustration.

A long-time fan of comics and graphic novels, Vincent has always wanted to create sequential art to tell a story of his own. He illustrated children's books for three years before joining the art department at Blue Sky Studios. This book gave him the opportunity to draw and paint all the cool stuff he's always wanted, with the exception of Aquaman riding a six-headed seahorse.

www.vincentdi.com

DAISUKE TSUTSUMI

Born and raised in the beautiful country of anime and karaoke, Daisuke "Dice" Tsutsumi was determined to become a baseball player at an early age. When faced with the reality that he wasn't actually that good, he migrated to America to look for something else to do.

After receiving irresponsible compliments from his nice and old retired classmates at his first painting class in a small community college in NY, he decided to define his American dream as making a living painting pretty pictures. Once he graduated from the School of Visual Arts, he worked for Lucas Learning LTD and now works for Blue Sky Studios painting a lot of pretty pitcures .

www.simplestroke.com

Thank YOU for buying this book.

We would all like to express a HUGE thank you to Chris Wedge who played quite a large role in bringing all of us together.

Also, many thanks go out to our friends and co-workers for their encouragement and interest in this book. They helped keep us motivated while we worked on it for such a long time.

And finally, to Pierre - thank you so much for taking us on and helping us get this book out! We couldn't have done it without you!

Andrea would like to thank... I want to thank my beautiful wife Alexandra and my little daughter Vanessa for their patience and love. To my fellow " Out of picture" artists and friends, who gave me the opportunity to be part of this amazing book (a big "Kiss" to Dice and Mike) and a big thank you to you readers for buying this book . Sounds like the Oscars, doesn't it?

Greg: I'd like to thank Dice, Bob, Vince, Mike and especially Chris Gilligan for all their help and advice.

Nash would like to thank his artistic compadres for their words of encouragement and cajoling throughout the whole OOP endeavor. Huge thanks to mom, Lynda Dunnigan, ("worlds greatest teacher") for her conversations on politics and US history. Big thanks also to Brenda Fairbairn at Lafayette High School, and Dr. William E. Blake at VCU.   Special thanks to Marina Dominis, for her encouragement and support. Lastly, thanks to Dice for his unwavering patience and friendship...

Dave: Thanks, Susie, for all your support.

Mike: Ellie, thanks for being so patient and for being a fresh set of eyes. Thanks to Ryan and all my book-mates for all the advice, crits, and inspiration. And especially my parents, who have always been an endless well of encouragement - thank you.

Benoit would like to thank his family and friends.

Daniel would like to thank Daisuke Tsutsumi for his inspiring leadership and Mike Knapp for his unparalleled craft. But most of all, Daniel wants to thank his beloved Kira, for her love and support. "I'm sorry we couldn't go to Cape Cod as much as you had wanted while this comic was getting done. I love you".

Bob would like to thank his family for their unconditional support, Alice Fung for her love and encouragement, Carol MacKenzie and Kathryn Otoshi for their advice, and all of his teachers, students, friends and fellow artists for inspiring him everyday.

Vince would like to thank Katherine Nix and Peter Nguyen.

Dice would like to thank Karin Komoto, Mika Tsutsumi, Rosalinda Malibiran, Teresa Shenberger, and Lara Zador.

OUT OF PICTURE

WWW.PAQUET.LI